This book belongs to

ISBN - 978-0-9982862-1-1

Published by Edible Rainbow project Press
Middletown, NY 10940

www.ediblerainbowproject.com

Anise Loves Red Food

For Claire and Eve
- Mama

For Olivia and Simão
- Mãe

This is Anise.
She's working hard on becoming a chef.
Today, she's busy planning Miss Catty's birthday menu. (Miss Catty is her favorite stuffy.)
It's going to be perfect!

That's her brother, Matisse. He's hungry so naturally, he looks for Anise.

"Any chance there's a pizza on that menu? I'm staaaaarving."
"Actually, I want to cook RED and pizza is on the list."
Matisse is relieved.
"Let's go look for some red food!"

In the kitchen, they're amazed at all the red they see.

2 quarts of strawberries,

1 bag of cherries,

1 quart of raspberries,

1 watermelon,

some rhubarb,

1 red pepper,

3 beautiful beets.

They look around some more and see tomatoes, apples, and quinoa.

"Time for mom and dad's cookbooks!"

"What's a hummus wrap?" asks Matisse.

" It looks yummy. Chickpeas blended with tahini, then spread on a wrap and rolled! " reads Anise.

They look over more recipes: beet chips, gazpacho, crepes...

Anise realizes they need some GREEN food like cucumber, herbs, and something leafy green for the wraps.

"Let's go to the market," suggests Anise. Before Matisse can object she's headed for the door, cloth bags in hand.

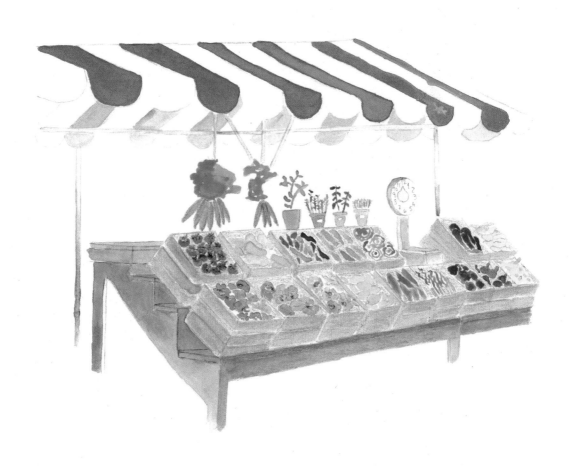

At the market, they see a rainbow of colors.

Red, orange, yellow, green, purple!

Anise is inspired. She wants everything to be just right.

"Oh, baby spinach is perfect for the
wraps!"

Matisse finds the cucumbers.

Back home Anise washes vegetables while Matisse is still hungry.

"Tell me about that gazpacho, Matisse."

"It's easy. Everything goes in the blender, then gets chilled."

"Do you want to make it?" Anise asks him.

"Me? Really?"

"YES!" exclaims Anise. "We have a lot of cooking to do; a soup, wraps, a cake!"

"A cake?!"

"I know it's a lot, but we can't have a birthday party without cake!"

"OK, I'll try to make the gazpacho."

"Wait." Anise stops Matisse in his tracks.

"Vanilla cake with strawberry-rhubarb compote or chocolate cake with raspberry frosting?"

"Anise, the answer is always chocolate cake. But what's compote?"

"It's just a fancy word for jam-like filling."

"Hmmm. That sounds interesting. I LOVE chocolate, but I'd like to try that compote, so let's have vanilla cake!"

"I've never made that one though," Anise worries.

But Matisse reassures her, "It's going to be great!"

In the kitchen, Matisse heads to the blender.
"I need cherries, tomatoes, a red and yellow bell pepper, and a cucumber."

Anise reads, but mostly she's lost in the smell of the baking beet chips and stewing strawberry and rhubarb.

Matisse, in his own world, has forgotten about the pizza for now because he can't believe how cool and crunchy all the vegetables are.

He also can't believe that gazpacho means "chilled soup".

So fancy!

Soon after:

The gazpacho goes chill, chill, chill.

The compote goes stew, stew, stew.

The cake batter goes whisk, whisk, whisk.

Slightly worried that they won't finish the menu, Anise remains focused.

Her chef's knife goes dice, dice, dice.

The pizza goes bake, bake, bake.

The frosting goes whip, whip, whip.

So far, things are moving along perfectly.

The crepes are rolled. The watermelon juice is ready. (Matisse got thirsty and wanted to drink red.)

Mom and Dad get home and smell the delicious food. They brought Anise (and Miss Catty) a little gift, the latest issue of Little Foodies magazine!

"Sweetheart, you've put together a lovely menu," Mom says.

"Thanks, Mama. Except my cake is crumbling." Anise lets a tear roll down her cheek when she sees the cake falling apart. "Can you help me fix it?"

"Hmmm. Let's try putting it in the freezer for a few minutes before we continue to tort.* That might work."

*To tort a cake is to divide it horizontally into layers so you can fill it.

In the meantime, Dad finds Matisse pouring gazpacho into glasses.

"What do you mean you eat soup from a glass, Matisse?"

"I know it looks strange, Dad, but trust me. Gazpacho is no ordinary soup."

So fancy.

Anise tries the cake again, but it's too late.

It's broken in three places.

Disappointment.

But there's no time.

She acts quickly and uses the frosting like glue to hold the cake together.

It's wobbly now.

Instead of a filling, the compote goes into a bowl as a side.

"Well, even broken cake can be delicious, right?" she sighs.

"So, what do you love about red food?" Dad asks them.

Anise goes first, "Red food makes me happy . There are vegetables and fruit that work together to make brand new flavors. It's so exciting!"

Matisse adds, "I love that pizza is red! Also, it goes really well with other colors like green and yellow."

"OK, let's eat!"

"Bon appétit," Anise says.

The family, Miss Catty, and stuffy friends sit around the table eating the delicious food. Everyone is looking forward to the cake, even though it's broken.

"Yum, Yum," says Matisse. "It's perfect, Anise, because we made it together."

Anise smiles.

Now, she's thinking about that cooking
contest she saw in her new magazine:

The Yellow and Orange Cook-off!

Can you cook with yellow and orange?

Anise knows she can and
she begins planning her menu.

RECIPES

Anise and Matisse are delighted to share some of the recipes they've found, created, and cooked together. These are their favorites. Which one is your favorite?

Red Lentil Soup
Cherry and Tomato Gazpacho
Veggie Quinoa Croquettes
Roasted Red Pepper Hummus Wraps
Margherita Pizza
Baked Beet Chips
Crunchy Red Granola
Buckwheat Crepes, Raspberry Chia Jam, Ricotta
Ladybug Cake with Strawberry Rhubarb Compote
Watermelon, Strawberry, Basil Juice
Berry Red Smoothie
Red Apple and Grape Salad

P.S. Anise wants you to know that
C=cup, T=tablespoon and t=teaspoon

Happy Cooking!

RED LENTIL SOUP

Serves a family of 4 with leftovers

You'll need:

2-3 T extra-virgin olive oil
1 yellow onion, diced (about 1 C)
2 cloves garlic, minced
1 T ground cumin
1 t ground coriander
¼ t ground turmeric
3 vine tomatoes, small dice with juice OR 1 (14 oz/400 g)
can of whole tomatoes, small dice
1 T tomato paste
1 C red lentils, rinsed
1 T honey
5 C water or veg stock
2 bay leaves
1 T apple cider vinegar
Sea salt, to taste
Cilantro, optional, for garnish
Creme fraiche, optional, for garnish

To Make:

1. In a saucepan, heat olive oil over medium heat and add onions and a pinch of salt. Cook for about 5 minutes until fragrant and translucent and then add garlic and cook for 3 more minutes.

2. Add spices and tomatoes with juices and stir to marry the flavors. Add the tomato paste after 5 minutes and finally the lentils and honey. Stir to mix.

3. Add ¼ C water (or stock) and deglaze the pot, letting cook for 2 minutes.

4. Finally, add the rest of the water (or stock) and the bay leaves. Cook over medium heat, partially covered for 25 minutes until lentils are soft.

4. About 5 minutes before lentils are done, add the vinegar and cook off.

5. Serve with a dollop of creme fraiche and some chopped cilantro. Some country bread would go very nice with this dish, too.

Vegan, Gluten-free

Cherry and Tomato Gazpacho

Makes about 4C

You'll need:

1 T plus 1/3 C extra-virgin olive oil
2 cloves garlic, crushed but kept whole
¼ C oats (optional)
1 sprig thyme or a pinch of dried thyme
250 g/ 1 C cherries, hulled and quartered
300 g/ 1 ¼ C tomatoes, chopped
2 small cucumbers, peeled, seeded, and diced (reserve 1 T for garnish)
½ red bell pepper, diced (reserve 1 T for garnish)
½ yellow bell pepper, diced (reserve 1 T for garnish)
1 T white balsamic vinegar
1 T lime juice
½ C water
Generous pinch of sea salt
2 T fresh basil, chopped (for garnish)

To Make:

1. Heat a small sauté pan over medium-high heat. Add 1T of the olive oil and 1 clove of garlic. When the garlic begins to sizzle, add the oats. Add the thyme and toss to coat oats completely. Cook for 2-3 minutes being careful not to let oats brown too much. Transfer the oats to a large bowl. Discard the garlic and thyme.
2. Add the tomatoes, strawberries, cucumber, peppers, remaining garlic clove, remaining 1/3 C of olive oil, vinegar, and salt to the bowl. Toss to combine and cover tightly with plastic wrap. Marinate at room temperature for 1-3 hours.

3. Blend the ingredients and their juices in small batches in a blender on high speed until very smooth. If it's too thick, add some water, 1 T at a time. Strain soup through cheesecloth or a sieve and chill in the refrigerator until very cold. Taste and adjust seasoning as necessary.
4. Top with diced vegetables and some basil leaves.

Vegan, Gluten-free

Veggie Quinoa Croquettes

Makes 24 croquettes

You'll need:

1 small sweet potato, large dice
2 T extra-virgin olive oil
1 small onion, small dice (about 1 C)
1 stalk celery, small dice (about 2 T)
1 t apple cider vinegar
1 egg, lightly beaten
2 C cooked red quinoa
2 T flat leaf parsley, finely chopped
1 t Himalayan salt (it's pink!) + more as needed
1 T tamari
3 T brown rice flour (or spelt flour if not GF)
½ C polenta or corn grits (or breadcrumbs)

To Make:

Preheat oven to 400° F/200° C

1. In a saucepan, bring 3 - 4 C water to a boil and add sweet potato. Boil for 20 minutes or until very tender (check with a fork). Drain and mash sweet potato in a large bowl. You should get about ¾ C of mashed sweet potato.

2. While the sweet potato is cooking, heat a sauté pan over medium heat and add the olive oil. Sauté the onions and celery with a pinch of salt until translucent and fragrant, about 8-10 minutes. Then, add apple cider vinegar and cook off for another 3 minutes.

3. Add onions and celery to sweet potato bowl and mix. Add quinoa, parsley, salt, tamari, and brown rice flour. Mix well until the mixture sticks fairly well.

5. With damp hands, form small oblong or round croquettes and roll each one in the polenta/corn grits/bread crumbs and place each croquette on a baking sheet with parchment paper.

6. Brush generously with olive oil and bake in the oven for 15 minutes or until golden brown, then roll croquettes over and bake for 10-15 more minutes until golden and crispy. Sometimes a third rotation for 10 minutes will do wonders for crispness.

7. Serve over fresh greens and avocado.

Vegan, Gluten-free

Roasted Red Pepper Hummus Wraps

Serves 4-6

You'll need:

¾ C dried chickpeas, soaked overnight and cooked through
with 1 bay leaf and 2 cloves of crushed garlic (OR 2 cans chickpeas)
1 clove garlic, finely grated
1/3 C fresh lemon juice, plus more as needed
½ - 1 t sea salt
¾ C tahini
1 red pepper, roasted
½ C ice water
1/3 C extra-virgin olive oil
1 t ground cumin
6 tortilla wraps (flour or corn)
Raw vegetables such as cucumbers, carrots, peppers, lettuce,
tomatoes, avocados to fill wraps

To Make:

1. If cooking chickpeas; Place chickpeas in a medium bowl and pour in cold water to cover by 2in/5cm. Cover and let sit overnight. Drain chickpeas, rinse, and place in a large sauce-pan along with smashed garlic and bay leaf. Pour in cold water to cover by 2in/5cm. Bring to a boil over medium-high heat; reduce heat and simmer gently, skimming foam that rises to the surface, until chickpeas are falling apart, 35–45 minutes. Drain and reserve 1 C cooking liquid. Discard garlic and bay leaf.
2. Combine grated garlic, lemon juice, and a pinch of salt in a food processor or blender and let sit for about 5 minutes to let the garlic mellow out.

3. Add tahini, roasted red pepper and ½ C ice water and process/blend until smooth. With the motor running, slowly stream in oil. Season with a large pinch of salt.

4. Add chickpeas and cumin and process until hummus is smooth, light, creamy, and dreamy, about 2 minutes. It will thicken as it cools, so it should be a bit loose at this stage. If it looks thick, thin with chickpea cooking liquid, pulsing in by the tablespoonful until you reach the right consistency.

5. Spread evenly over tortilla wraps, fill with veggies of choice and then roll to make wrap.

Vegetarian

Margherita Pizza

Makes 2 -10" pizzas
*Weighing the ingredients yields the best results.

You'll need:

175 g (1 1/2C) semolina flour
180 g (1 1/2C) spelt flour
8 g (1t) fine Himalayan salt
2 g (¾ t) active dry yeast
4 - 8g (1t -2t) extra-virgin olive oil + more for
brushing
1 T water, lukewarm

For the sauce/ topping:

1 clove garlic, minced
¼ C yellow onion, finely diced
1 t dried oregano
½ t dried basil
½ -1 t Himalayan salt
400 g/14oz (about 1 ½ C) crushed tomatoes or puree
2 C shredded mozzarella
Fresh basil leaves for garnish

To Make:

1. In a large bowl, mix the flours and salt.
2. In a small bowl, stir together the water and the yeast. Let it sit until it gets foamy. around
minutes. Then, add the olive oil.
3. Add wet mixture to dry mixture and mix until well combined. Once the dough comes
together, knead/shape into a ball and let the dough rest for about 2 - 3 mins.
4. Knead dough for another 5 minutes, then cut dough into 2 equal pieces and shape each

into a ball. Place each ball on a floured surface (a plate or the counter) and cover with a dampened cloth. Let the dough rest and rise for 90 minutes at room temperature. It can also rest in the refrigerator for up to 24 hours. If refrigerating the dough, give yourself time to let the dough rest at room temperature for 30 to 45 minutes.

5. To make pizza, place each dough ball on a heavily floured surface and use your fingers to stretch it, then your hands to shape it into rounds or squares. You could also use a rolling pin to roll it out.

To Make the sauce:
Preheat oven to at least 500 F/260 C .
1. In a small saucepan heat the olive oil over low-medium heat and add onions, garlic, spices and salt.
2. When translucent and aromatic, add the tomato sauce and let simmer for 5 minutes.
3. Top pizza dough evenly with 1 C of sauce and 1 C of cheese.
4. Place pizza on the middle rack in the oven (on a HOT pizza stone would be ideal) and let bake for 10-12 minutes until cheese is melted and crust looks crispy.

* Tips: Try to get the dough to be thin so that it cooks through and isn't doughy.

Vegetarian

Baked Beet Chips

Makes a big, happy bowlful

You'll need:

3 medium-large beets, sliced super thin
1 T extra-virgin olive oil
1 t sea salt, in flakes if available
Pinch of freshly ground black pepper
Dried herbs such as basil or rosemary, optional

To Make:

1. Line 2 baking sheets with parchment paper (or you can bake in batches).
2. Wash and dry beets and slice ever so thinly, about 1/16inch or 2 mm thick. It's very possible to do with a sharp knife (and great for practicing knife skills) however a mandoline slicer makes this much easier.
3. Place sliced beets in a bowl and drizzle oil on beets, massaging the oil into each beet chip to ensure that they are coated but not excessively.
4. Arrange chips to sit next to each other without overlapping on the sheet pans and bake at 350º F/180º C for 20-25 minutes. Start to pay close attention at the 15 minute mark. Every oven is different and some may need to be rotated.
5. When just browned around the edges, remove from oven and sprinkle with sea salt, pepper and herbs, if using. Let the chips cool on the sheet pan for 10 minutes.

Vegan, Gluten-free

Crunchy Red Granola (Makes 8 C)

You'll need:

1 C popped amaranth (about 1/4 C + 2 T unpopped amarranth) (optional)

2 C gluten free oats

1 C almonds, roughly chopped

1/2 C walnuts, roughly chopped

1/4 C unsweetened shredded coconut

1/4 C sunflower seeds

2T hemp seeds

1 t ground cinnamon

1/2 t freshly grated nutmeg

1/2 t sea salt

3 T extra-virgin coconut oil

3 T extra-virgin olive oil

1/4 C raw honey

2 T maple syrup

1 C dried cranberries, cherries, raspberries

To Make:

1. To pop amaranth: Heat a sauté pan over medium/high heat and put a pinch of amaranth in to test for temperature. Once they begin to pop, the pan is hot enough. Add 1-2 T at a time and cover with a mesh splatter screen because these will POP!

2. Mix all dry ingredients (amaranth, oats, nuts, coconut, seeds, spices) in a large bowl.

3. Heat oil and sweeteners in a small saucepan over low heat. Once everything is combined and melted, pour it over oat mixture and mix well.

4. Spread on prepared sheet pan and bake for 15 minutes in 300ºF / 150ºC .

5. Stir granola and add dried fruit. Increase temperature to 325ºF/ 160ºC and bake for 15 more minutes keeping an eye so it doesn't burn. It will be a beautiful, golden brown color.

6. Let cool before storing in mason jars.

Buckwheat Crepes, Raspberry Chia Jam, Ricotta

Makes 1 dozen large crepes

You'll need:

2 eggs
1 2/3 C milk (or coconut or nut milk)
¼ t sea salt
140g brown rice flour (about 1 C)
125g tapioca starch (about 1 C)
30g buckwheat flour (about ¼ C)
2 T butter (or coconut oil) for cooking crepes

To Make:

1. Crack the eggs, separately into a cup and add milk and salt, then pour into a blender.
2. Mix the dry ingredients making sure it's mixed well and add to the blender.
3. Blend until all mixed and smooth. Batter should be thin.
4. Heat a cast iron skillet on medium heat and melt butter/oil. Spoon in about ¼ C of batter (make sure the skillet is hot) then use the handle to swirl the batter around so the bottom is covered in batter.
5. Cook on one side for 2-3 minutes or until just golden. Flip and do the same for about 1-2 minutes.

Vegetarian, Gluten-free

Raspberry Chia Jam

Makes 2 C

You'll need:

1 C (280g) frozen raspberries
2 T + 2 t (24g) chia seeds
1 T freshly squeezed orange juice
1 T freshly squeezed lemon juice (about ½ a lemon-Meyer lemons work well here)
¼ C raw honey
1 t lemon zest

To Make:

1. Place raspberries in a saucepan over low-medium heat. Add chia seeds, orange and lemon juice and let cook until the raspberries have completely thawed and you're left with a runny mixture.
2. Add honey and zest and mix well. When cool, add to two jam mason jars and refrigerate. The jam will set after about 4 hours or overnight.
3. If it's still too runny for you, add more chia seeds one teaspoon at a time until desired consistency is reached.
4. Fresh jam will keep up to a week in the fridge and can be frozen for up to 2 months.

To Serve:

1. Spread jam on a crepe and either roll it or fold it in half. If using ricotta, place a dollop on top and drizzle with a touch more honey.

Vegan, Gluten-free

Ladybug Cake

Makes 1-2 layer 8" cake

You'll need:

DRY:

220 g (2 C) Gluten-free flour (Use a flour that has a blend of at least some brown and white rice flour, potato starch, and tapioca starch.)
60 g (½ C) oat flour
1 T ground flax seeds
80 g (2/3 C) organic coconut sugar
45 g (1/3 C) organic brown sugar
2 t baking powder
½ t baking soda
½ t Himalayan salt
1 t ground cinnamon

WET:

1 2/3 C almond milk or other non-dairy milk (regular milk is also ok if dairy isn't an issue)
1 T apple cider vinegar
1/3 C melted coconut oil (or melted butter)
2 T organic vanilla extract

To Make:

1. Preheat oven to 350F/180C and oil and flour an 8" cake pan.
2. Sift dry ingredients together in a bowl and whisk together.
3. Place almond milk and apple cider vinegar in a measuring cup and set aside for 5 minutes.
4. In a separate bowl, whisk together wet ingredients and pour into dry mixture. Mix well so there are no clumps and to aerate the batter. (You can't really overmix a gluten-free batter since there is no gluten to worry about.)
5. Pour batter into the prepared cake pan.
6. Bake for about 40-50 minutes until the cake is springy to touch and the edges pull away from the sides of the pan.
7. Allow to cool in the pan on a wire rack for 10 minutes before removing and letting cool completely on the rack.

Strawberry Rhubarb Compote

Makes 2 C (maybe more)
You'll need:
250g/ 1C rhubarb, roughly chopped
300g/ 1 ¼ C strawberries, fresh or thawed frozen (raspberries are gorgeous, too)
½ C unsweetened grape juice
¼ C juice from tangerine (or orange)
1t lemon zest
1 cinnamon stick
2 T honey
½ C coconut sugar

To Make:

1. Place all ingredients in a small saucepan over low-medium heat and let cook until it becomes very liquid.

2. Adjust heat to low and let simmer partially covered for 20-30 minutes or until it's thickened* enough that you can spread it. It will thicken as it cools, too.

*Tip: If compote is too liquidy, you could make a slurry. Put 1 T of arrowroot starch (or organic corn starch) in a small bowl. Add 3-4 T of the compote liquid to the arrowroot and combine well. Add this slurry to the pot and cook through for 5 minutes.

**If filling cupcakes, fill cupcake liners halfway with batter, then add 1-1 ½ t compote and fill the rest with more batter.

Strawberry Frosting

You'll need:
1 C coconut butter, softened or grass-fed butter (200g)
½ C raw honey
2 ½ C icing sugar
1 ½ C arrowroot starch
1 t vanilla
1 T non-dairy milk (or milk if using butter)
1 C freeze-dried strawberries, ground (or raspberries)
1 t beet powder (optional, for a deeper red color)

To Make:
1. Place coconut butter or butter in a large bowl of a stand mixer or a large bowl if using an electric mixer.
2. Add honey first, then add icing sugar ½ C at a time, alternating with arrowroot starch, mixing until fully incorporated before adding more.
3. Finally, add vanilla, (non-dairy) milk, freeze-dried berries, and beet powder, if using. Mix thoroughly until a dreamy, creamy frosting appears.

*If using coconut butter, you may need to add a bit of water, 1 t at a time to reach the desired consistency.

Watermelon, Strawberry, Basil Juice

Makes 6 C

You'll need:

500g (about 4C) watermelon, diced
150g (about 1C) strawberries, hulled
2 C unsweetened pomegranate juice
1 T lime juice
2 T maple syrup
basil leaves, plus a few more for garnish

To Make:

1. Place all ingredients in a blender and blend until super smooth. Serve chilled or over ice with basil leaves for garnish.

Berry Red Smoothie

Makes 5 C

You'll need:

1 C hibiscus tea
225g (1 ½ C) strawberries
150g (1C) raspberries
1 banana
½ peach
¼ C freshly squeezed orange juice
1 T raw honey
1 T hemp seeds
1 C coconut milk

*You can use frozen fruit for this recipe. If you're using fresh fruit, be sure to add at least 6 ice cubes to make it thick and creamy.

To Make:

1. Boil 1 C of water to brew hibiscus tea for 5 minutes. Let cool.
2. Place all ingredients in a high speed blender and blend until creamy, red, and delicious.

Red Apple and Grape Salad

By Kaden Hubly

Seves 4

You'll need:

3 red apples, diced (Empire, Cortland, Fuji and Pink Lady apples work great here.)
1 ½ C red seedless grapes, halved
2 T raw honey

Optional ingredients:

¼ C pomegranate kernels
1-2 T freshly squeezed orange juice
5 mint leaves, finely sliced

To Make:

1. In a small bowl combine grapes and apples.
2. Drizzle honey over and stir gently. You can even toss with your hands.
3. Refrigerate and enjoy. Serve at room temperature or refrigerate.

*If using optional ingredients, include all of them in step 1.
(except for the nuts... those go on last).

The End

ABOUT THE AUTHOR
Nathalie Curabba, MS, CNS

Nathalie is a clinical nutritionist, health-supportive chef, and author of Anise Loves Green Food. She consults, teaches, and writes about food and nutrition. She can usually be found in the kitchen with her 2 wonderful daughters and amazing husband, each with their own station and incredible culinary ideas.
Find her online at www.nathaliecurabba.com

ABOUT THE ILLUSTRATOR
Marta Côrte-Real

Marta has been an art and outdoors lover since she can remember, which is the reason she became a landscape architect. She is a wife and a mother of two young and energetic children who love books and are her daily inspiration to illustrate for small children.
Find her online at 🅞 lemonmintillustration.